SHARKS
off Cornwall & Devon

C000063164

Richard Peirce

TOR MARK - REDRUTH

For further information of all the titles in this series please visit:-
www.tormark.co.uk

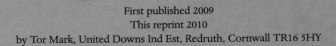

First published 2009
This reprint 2010
by Tor Mark, United Downs Ind Est, Redruth, Cornwall TR16 5HY

ISBN 978 085025 417 4   © 2009 Tor Mark

Design Alix Wood: www.alixwood.co.uk

Acknowledgements

Front cover: Blue shark - Richard Peirce
Back cover: The author holding a bait tube - Richard Peirce
This page: Blue shark close-up off Cornwall - Mark Boothman
Illustrations for Cornwall & Devon Shark Directory - © Per Larsen

All other images are copyright of the author unless stated in the captions.

Printed by R Booth Ltd, The Praze, Penryn, Cornwall TR10 8AA

Introduction

For decades Cornwall and Devon's beaches have been popular attractions for holidaymakers from all over Britain. I suspect that very few bathers, surfers, divers, and other water users realise that they share these waters with sharks. Names like Mako, Blue shark, Thresher, Hammerhead and others would by most be thought of as alien to our waters. This book will introduce you to our sharks and put the threat they pose into perspective.

I hope when you've met our sharks you'll want to get close to them, and that shark eco-tourism may become another reason you visit Cornwall and Devon. The beasts of Bodmin and Exmoor are, I suspect, fictional whereas sharks in Cornish and Devon waters are fact. I hope you enjoy meeting them.

RICHARD PEIRCE, North Cornwall.

Chapter 1: The World of Sharks

hark. There are few words that send a shiver down the spine so successfully. Peter Benchley's book *Jaws*, later made into a blockbuster film by Steven Spielberg, identified man's fears and played on them. The fear of being eaten alive, the fear of being outside your element and the fear of the unknown are all exploited menacingly in the early minutes of the film, when the first victim falls prey to attack. What can be more chilling than swimming on the surface of the ocean wondering what unseen dangers are lurking beneath you? This is the stuff of nightmares and truly terrifying.

By the start of the 20th century, sharks were firmly established as fearsome and loathsome predators. Shipwreck incidents in both world wars reconfirmed this outlook. When the USS Indianapolis was sunk in the Far East at the end of World War II, 900 men went into the water, but only 317 survived the sharks and the elements. Thereafter, the shark's position as a hate figure equalled that of any monster before or since.

There are at least 456 shark species in the world's oceans and around 30 can be found in British seas, and more than half of them are present off Cornwall and Devon. Of the United Kingdom's shark species only the Mako, Blue, Thresher and Porbeagle are recorded as being dangerous to man. However, with these species being depleted by more than 60 per cent due to overfishing, having the chance to see such magnificent animals must be regarded as a privilege, not something to provoke fear and media hysteria. Many will be surprised to learn that – in addition to Makos, Blues, Threshers, and Porbeagles – Hammerheads, Soupfin sharks (Tope), Sixgill and Sevengill sharks are also on the Cornwall and Devon list.

Sharks possess the same five senses as humans – smell, taste, touch, hearing and sight – although, in some instances, they work relatively better in their world than ours do in our environment. Experiments with Lemon and Nurse sharks have established their olfactory ability to detect concentrations as low as one part per million. When working with Blue sharks off north Cornwall, I lay 'chum' in the water. This is essentially a

The second largest fish in the world, the Basking shark, is commonly found off Cornwall and Devon's coasts. When conditions are right this shark is often seen from cliff tops. (see page 26)   (COLIN SPEEDIE)

scent trail made of mashed up oily fish such as mackerel, the Westcountry name for chum is 'rubby dubby'. I very often have to wait several hours for Blue sharks to find us. This not only illustrates their relative scarcity, but also indicates that, for our trail to be effective, we have to wait for it to cover several miles. When sharks have picked up the smell, they will swim up the trail looking for a meal. The concentration of chum materials in the water two or three miles from the boat is minute but the sharks still find us, thereby illustrating their acute sense of smell.

In addition to the five senses they share with us, sharks also have two extra senses: the lateral line, a mechanosensory system, and the ampullae of Lorenzini, an electrosensory system.

The lateral line extends from the head to the base of the tail (caudal) fin, and consists of a pair of tubes containing sets of sensory cells with protrusions known as neuromasts or hair cells. The hairs react to movement and changes in pressure. Working in conjunction with the lateral line are the pit organs, which are pockets scattered around the body that also contain sensory cells. These systems enable sharks to detect changes in pressure, tiny vibrations and water displacements, and to determine the directions from which they are coming.

The ampullae of Lorenzini make up an electrosensory system used to detect weak electrical fields. Elongated, jelly-filled tubes connect pores on the skin's surface to the ampullae, which contain receptor cells. These pores are clearly visible as dark dots below the snout and behind the eyes. I have many times seen Great White sharks apparently attracted to, and investigating, metal items such as propellers and shark cages. This is quite possibly due to the object's electrical field. It is believed that Hammerheads may use a combination of their electrosensory and mechanosensory systems to detect prey buried in sand.

Sharks are superbly adapted to their environment. Light pliable cartilage tissue instead of heavy dense bones, together with their highly streamlined shapes, promotes efficient movement. Different species hunt in different ways; our warm-blooded sharks such as the Mako, Thresher and Porbeagle often rely on speed to catch their prey. Others such as the Angel sharks are ambush predators and depend on their camouflage to conceal them. The Thresher uses its giant tail to gather baitfish into dense shoals which it then attacks, and the Basking shark filter feeds as it passes through plankton.

Sharks are carnivores with diets ranging from plankton to mammals, other sharks, large and small bony fish and invertebrates, including crustaceans. The dental array of sharks reflects this diet. The filter feeders (plankton eaters) have only tiny vestigial teeth, whereas the Great White has a formidable set of sharp triangular teeth perfectly suited to removing large chunks of flesh from their prey. The Mako has sharp, pointed, blade-like teeth ideal for tearing and trapping prey. Ocean bottom-dwelling sharks, which have crustaceans on their menu, have specialised teeth for crushing shells. A shark's mouth is a tooth factory, with new teeth being continuously formed in the gums inside the mouth and then moving outwards. The older teeth drop off making space for the new, which may last for anything from a month to a year.

Sharks breathe by extracting oxygen from the water as it passes over their gills. Water enters through the mouth, passes through the internal gill openings and is then expelled through the external gill outlet. There's less oxygen in water than in air, so sharks need to ensure a good, continual flow through their gills. Some species achieve this by using a system called 'ram ventilation', which forces water through the gills as the shark swims. Others rely on a combination of ram ventilation and a gill pump and often spend time motionless – either resting or 'sleeping' on the sea floor – while the pump provides the flow of oxygenated water over their gills.

There are over 30 species of sharks present in British waters and of these at least sixteen are found off Cornwall and Devon's coasts. There is great variety in our sharks which range from the giant Basking shark achieving lengths of over 30 foot (10 metres) to the wonderful little 18in (0.45 metres) Smallspotted Catshark, between the two are names to stir the blood like Mako, Thresher shark, Blue shark, Porbeagle and Hammerhead (a full illustrated list of our sharks appears at the end of this book). The big question is do Great White sharks visit Cornwall and Devon. We will explore this in the next chapter.

Chapter 2: Great Whites – Yes or No?

Why isn't the Great White shark a permanent resident in British waters? Conditions are broadly similar to those where large resident populations flourish, such as South Africa, southern Australia, and California. The nearest confirmed Great White shark to our waters was the capture in 1977 of a female in the Northern Bay of Biscay off La Rochelle – 168 nautical miles from Land's End. In 2003/04, a female Great White nicknamed Nicole completed a six-month, 13,000+ mile journey from False Bay in South Africa to Western Australia, where she turned around and then swam back to South Africa. So, clearly, 168 miles is no distance for these sharks.

Fishermen's stories are renowned for their colour and exaggeration. By the mid 1990s, I realised that I was continually hearing stories of large, powerful, unidentified sharks in UK waters. Could some of them be Great Whites? There was no reason why not, so I started logging each report.

My record keeping has not included all the reports I have received, because some claimed sightings were so ludicrous they weren't worth noting or considering further. However, from 1996 until the time of writing I can certainly say that I have heard of between 70 and 80 possible Great White shark encounters. Of those, seven that I have investigated remain credible after further examination. I am not saying that these seven incidents involved Great Whites, but the descriptions given certainly fit those of Great White sharks.

So do these sharks visit our shores or not? The jury is out and will remain so until firm proof exists – a carcass, tooth, tissue sample, photograph or some other conclusive evidence. However, there is a high probability that the creatures involved in some of the following incidents were indeed Great White sharks.

LOOE, CORNWALL: JULY 1970

John Reynolds, a Looe-based shark angling skipper, had been at sea all day about eight miles offshore with baited lines out and two rubby dubby bags dangling in the water. In that year Porbeagle and Blue shark numbers were much higher than they are now, so it was unusual that they had not seen one all day. John's theory is that the lack of sharks might have indicated the presence of a larger predator.

At sometime around 3.00 p.m. John started to take in his lines and rubby dubby bags in preparation for returning to shore. He was pulling in the stern bag when a large shark appeared only a few feet behind the boat.

The animal looked straight at John, staying in a head-up position for some seconds before slipping back into the water and disappearing. John saw only the head but his description fits a Great White shark and it is the only shark commonly known to spy-hop, which is the action of putting its head out of the water. Spy-hopping has rarely been observed in non-baited conditions and may not be natural behaviour. Current opinion suggests it is a response to concentrated scent stimuli at the surface like chum lines, and not an attempt to espy objects above the surface as has been previously thought. Spy-hopping is also practised by some whales but I have never heard of any of our existing shark species doing this.

The incident described by John fits a Great White shark spy-hopping.

PADSTOW, NORTH CORNWALL: AUGUST 1999

A leaked tip-off to the national press about the sighting of a large shark thought to be a Great White up the coast from Padstow near Crackington Haven resulted in a hysterical reaction and, at times, insulting scepticism. This combination made the fishing party involved dismayed that the story ever got out.

Mike Turner and Phil Britts, who were aboard the *Blue Fox* together with Phil's wife, Rhona, and others all saw a large shark about 37 metres (40 yards) away. The dorsal fin was clearly visible approaching them in a

Why Britain doesn't have a Great White shark population
is a puzzle as conditions are ideal.

(RICHARD PEIRCE)

straight line as they were releasing an earlier-caught Soupfin shark (Tope).

The shark, estimated to be 4.6 metres (15ft) long, passed the stern and rolled, revealing a clear white underside separated from the grey/brown topside by a jagged line. It was visible for about a minute, having, at its nearest, come within two metres of the boat. Those on board believed that it had probably taken the Soupfin shark (Tope) before disappearing.

A large black eye was noted and this, together with the colours and shape described, are consistent with a Great White shark. Mike had seen many Great Whites in South Africa and is adamant about the precision of his sighting. The others on board had seen a number of Porbeagles and Basking sharks and ruled those out. It is noted that the proactive behaviour displayed in approaching the boat also fits the actions of a Great White shark.

CAMBEAK HEAD, NORTH CORNWALL: AUGUST 1999

The *Blue Fox* incident took place off Cambeak Head, and the following day there was a similar occurrence in exactly the same location. Paul Vincent was out with his friend Jason Coe fishing for Soupfin shark (Tope) from his 5.2 metre (17 foot) Dory, *Blissful*. Paul had hooked a Soupfin shark (Tope) and was about to lift it aboard using his gaff hook when a very large shark appeared and bit off the bottom two thirds of the Soupfin shark (Tope) before swimming off. Paul estimates that it was at least as long as his boat. His full description was a match for the shark seen by those aboard the *Blue Fox*: the same grey/brown dorsal side, white ventral side, large triangular dorsal fin, black eye and unhurried, investigative behaviour.

TINTAGEL HEAD, NORTH CORNWALL: SEPTEMBER 1999

Less than two weeks after these incidents and about 12 miles away near Tintagel Head, a lobster fisherman found a very large shark tangled up in his rope. He asked to remain anonymous – although his identity is known to me – and the whole incident I am about to describe was witnessed. When hauling in his pots there was what he thought was a snag in the line. It freed and then something hit the back of the winching gear. He went to look and saw the tail fin of a shark about 4.6 metres (15ft) long. Because of its size, he thought it must be a Basking shark.

Sharks cannot swim backwards and, if they land up in a rope, they often twist and become thoroughly entangled. Death follows unless they are freed quickly, and, unfortunately that was the fate of this creature. As it had no commercial value, the only thing to do was to cut it loose. It was seen to have a slate grey topside and, as it was freed, it rolled showing a pure white underside. It also had what were described as a crescent-shaped mouth and triangular teeth. Basking sharks and Porbeagles were both familiar to those on board and they were sure it was neither of those. At 4.6 metres (15ft) what else could it have been? A Blue shark or a Porbeagle? Very unlikely. A Mako? Again unlikely, and the colours and teeth as described don't fit.

So, three sharks each estimated to be the same size, each broadly fitting the same description and their sightings separated by only three weeks and 12 miles. Coincidence? Same shark? A Great White shark?

QUIES ISLANDS, NORTH CORNWALL: JULY 2002

On a clear, almost windless day Brian Bate was laying his lobster pots to the northeast of the Quies Islands, when, suddenly, a large fish between 3.6 metres (12ft) and 4.6 metres (15ft) in length leapt completely out of the water with something in its mouth. Brian went to the spot and found a large spreading pool of blood with pieces of seal blubber floating in it. Seagulls were already feeding on the smaller pieces of blubber.

Leaping out of the water is called breaching and what Brian saw was a typical breaching attack, the size, body shape and colours precisely fitting a Great White shark. When I showed him various photographs of breaching sharks, including those of Makos and Threshers, he identified the Great White.

I suggested to him that it was a pity he hadn't retrieved one of the larger pieces of blubber in case a tooth might have been lodged in it or the bite mark could have been identified. He told me that he didn't have a boathook and no sane person who had seen what he had would have started putting their hands in the water fishing around for bits of blubber!

If it wasn't a Great White, what else could it have been? For various reasons based on Brian's description, Blues, Porbeagles and Makos can be ruled out, which leaves a Killer Whale (Orca) as the only other possibility. Brian had seen many Orcas and was quite sure that wasn't the case.

The triangular teeth of a Great White shark and the sawing action of the jaws make dismemberment a typical occurrence; this does not happen with the other sharks mentioned.

Two days after Brian Bate saw his 'breaching shark' kill a seal, a lone yachtsman sailed up the coast from Newquay to Padstow. He later recounted how a large shark followed in his wake for the greater part of his journey and how he had sailed through the same water where Brian had seen the breaching attack. He is familiar with Basking Shark fins and is certain the shark that followed him was not one of those.

I went chumming in the Quies area with Brian two weeks after the seal attack and there were no seals to be seen where, normally, there is a small colony of between 15 and 20. The general area around Trevose Head, the Quies, the Camel Estuary and the offshore islands is home to several small population pockets of seals, but they did not return to the area until early October. I was alerted to two cases of washed-up seal remains, one in July before the Bates incident and the other in early August. Both carcasses consisted of only partial remains and both were extensively bird-pecked, making it impossible to determine how the seals died or learn anything from the wounds.

ST IVES, CORNWALL: JULY 2007

On Thursday 26 July, Dr Oliver Crimmen was shown a clip of amateur video by the *Sun* newspaper. It was taken on a video camcorder by Nick Fletcher while holidaying in St Ives. The film showed a small pod of Common dolphins making their way along the coast and, at the end of the sequence, a creature is clearly seen to breach. Dr Crimmen was quoted as saying: "It's definitely predatory and definitely big. I can't rule out a Great White."

I, too, was asked to confirm the identity. But it was impossible because the film was not clear enough. All that could be seen for sure was that it was a fish somewhere between 2.4 metres (8ft) and 3.6 metres (12ft) long doing a half-to-three-quarters breach displaying a white ventral side. Given the close presence of dolphins, they must come into the reckoning as must Basking, Porbeagle and Mako sharks.

If, as I do, you believe that Great Whites are occasional visitors to our shores then that possibility cannot be ruled out. However, saying they can't be ruled out is a long way from confirming that the image showed a Great White shark, which is what the *Sun* inferred that I had done.

This sparked an extraordinary media frenzy and the *Sun* managed to string it out for a further eight days with all the other nationals and many regional papers joining in. Both the Monday and Tuesday editions of the *Sun* carried front page pictures of Basking shark's dorsal fins slicing through the waters off St Ives with various 'experts' identifying the fins as belonging to Great Whites. By Thursday, the *Newquay Guardian*'s front page carried a picture of a Great White said to be taken off Towan Head, Newquay. This was the first picture of a Great White to appear, but interest was waning and various other reports were hinting at doubts over where the photograph was taken. The photograph was later admitted to be a hoax.

During this time, the people of St Ives were, understandably, cashing in. Shark spotting boat trips were packed with excited tourists. Virtually everything that could float was taking to the sea to look for sharks. Cafés had maps of St Ives Bay on their walls with all the sightings marked. Shark ice creams, T-shirts and even shark-shaped pasties were produced to add to the fun and make the tills ring more frequently.

Nick Fletcher's original film clip had been forgotten by the time the story died. This was probably the most intense and long-running shark saga ever in the UK press, but was by no means based on compelling evidence.

The question remains: do Great White sharks ever visit British waters? For me, the answer is 'probably yes'. However, there is still no hard evidence and, owing to the massive depletion rates the species has suffered (about 80 per cent), the chances of any such visit are slim and getting slimmer.

Great White shark
(CHRIS FALLOWS)

Chapter 3: Cornish Shark Angling

Very few holidaymakers who visited Cornwall in 1961 are likely to have been aware that 6,300 sharks were caught by anglers off the county's coasts that year. It was the highest annual number ever recorded by the Shark Angling Club (SAC) based in Looe. Most of the catch were Blue sharks, but in those days Mako, Porbeagle and Thresher sharks were also caught regularly on rod and line.

The founding of the Shark Angling Club quickly established Looe as the 'shark capital' of Britain, and, in the 1950s and 1960s, its shark angling fleet consisted of 20 full-time boats during the June to October season. Mevagissey, Polperro, Porthleven, Newlyn and Penzance also had shark angling fleets, and boats started working from Padstow, Boscastle and Bude on the north Cornish coast, as well as out of north and south Devon and some ports in Dorset.

Since 1961, Looe Shark Angling Club figures for shark catches have crashed and, in 2008, only 152 Blue sharks were caught. The regular incidence of Mako, Porbeagle and Threshers has now become sporadic. There is no Shark Angling Club record of a Mako being caught since the 1970s and a juvenile Porbeagle caught in 2002 was the first caught by a club boat for many years. Juvenile Threshers caught in 2005 and 2007 were also the first for several years. In fact, all of the species targeted by anglers in Westcountry waters have suffered severe population declines owing to commercial fishing pressures.

CHANGING TIMES

In the 1960s in Looe it must have seemed as if the seas produced an endless supply of sharks. On most evenings during the season visitors to the quayside would have seen sharks hanging up outside the Shark Angling Club, where they were weighed and photographed with their captors. The following day most of the sharks were taken out to sea and dumped. In the 1960s and 1970s annual SAC catches of between 2,000 and 4,000 were usual. Throughout that period the club fleet comprised 18–20 boats, all of which spent most of the season engaged in sharking.

Mrs Yallop with her British record Mako in 1971. (SHARK ANGLING CLUB)

Change was on the way, though, and it arrived in 1976, when a catch of 928 was recorded compared with 2083 the previous year. This dramatic reduction of more than 50 per cent from one year to the next heralded a decline in numbers that bottomed out at 86 caught in the year 2000. However, shark angling is not responsible for the decline as numbers caught by anglers around the world are insignificant compared with the tens of millions taken by industrial fishing. Having said that, even before the "crash of 76" attitudes in Looe were changing with more and more sharks being released each year.

Between 1972 and 1976, the first tag-and-release programme was conducted as a joint effort by Dr John Stevens and the Shark Angling Club (the venture was part of Dr Stevens' Ph.D project) and 2,883 sharks – Blues, Soupfin Sharks (Tope), Porbeagles, and a Shortfin Mako – were tagged. Some years later the Jack Daniel's whiskey company took up sponsoring the next tag-and-release programme and all those returning tags with the requested information were rewarded with a bottle of whiskey. That sponsorship ended in 1995 and, from then on, all sharks caught were released unrecorded until tagging resumed under my sponsorship in August 1999.

To qualify to join the Shark Angling Club, an angler must land a shark weighing a minimum of 75lb (34kg). This used to mean that all sharks that appeared to attain that weight or more had to be killed and weighed to enable new members to qualify. But, as I mentioned, attitudes were changing, and, in 1994, the club passed new rules involving a formula that enabled skippers to estimate weight based on length and girth. This rule came in specifically to stop the need for killing, unless a record was suspected, in which case the fish still had to be weighed. Other than suspected records, the club now operates a 100 per cent release policy and most skippers take part in the tagging programme.

One seeming contradiction among hunters of animals on land and sea is the respect and affection in which they regard their quarry. So the question is: why catch it if you love it? I suspect that question would get 10 different answers from 10 different people but what would be uniform is the respect that I have observed first hand among 99 per cent of the shark anglers I know. One man who long lined large numbers of Porbeagles off Cornwall in December 2003 caused widespread condemna-

J Pottier with his 211kg Porbeagle caught in 1976.

(SHARK ANGLING CLUB)

tion, with shark anglers being among the loudest critics. In August 2007, another longliner caught more than 60 sharks near Lundy Island off the north Devon coast and he, too, was universally derided by anglers. Those who take up shark angling as a blood sport are quickly singled out by skippers and there is a virtual black list of people they will not take out again. Thankfully, it's a short list.

Changing attitudes have brought about differences to equipment, with the use of circle and barbless hooks now being the norm. Also, not all Looe skippers will tag sharks as some feel that removing the animals from the 'support' of the water causes damage to organs that can prove fatal. This is correct and most skippers bring only the smaller sharks

A Blue shark loses its battle. Nowadays the majority of sharks are released.
(SHARK ANGLING CLUB)

onboard, while tagging the larger ones over the side of the boat. All skippers are highly competent and hook removal, tagging, and measuring is done in the minimum of time. Survival rates among released Blue sharks is thought by the Shark Angling Club to be near 100 per cent, although it might possibly be less in the case of Porbeagles.

When a tagged shark is re-caught, the fisherman will find the tag has a 'message in a bottle system', which offers a $15 reward for letting the club know the length of the shark and the latitude and longitude of its re-catch position. As it happens, 99.9 per cent of returns are from Spanish longliners operating in the Bay of Biscay and between the Azores and the Canaries. However, in 2002, the club was told about a female Blue shark re-caught off the New Hampshire coast while other returns have come from the USA, South America and South Africa. Therefore, it can be clearly seen that tag and release helps establish migration patterns and provides information about growth rates.

Like others all over the world engaged in eco-tourism and leisure, the Shark Angling Club recognises the economic importance of sharks. The Great White shark has become a valued asset in the South African Western Cape and the Blue shark has been part of Looe's economy for 50 years. So the more it's recognised that sharks have a greater value alive rather than dead, the more recruits will swell conservationist ranks.

To recap:
• Six thousand sharks caught each year off Looe has become fewer than 200
• Eighteen full-time boats have decreased to 12 or 14 part-timers
• An almost total kill has become no kill
• The thriving drift net pilchard industry that attracted sharks and triggered them becoming targets for anglers has disappeared
• Hook sizes and designs have altered and angling club rules have changed
• Trophy photos have given way to tags

Hopefully, commercial fishing policies will now change, too, and shark numbers will start to recover. If they do, no organisation will be happier than the Shark Angling Club.

CHAPTER 4: Shark Eco-Tourism

Anglers have been travelling to Cornwall and Devon for over 50 years to catch our sharks so in a sense shark eco-tourism is not new, however today's eco-tourist is more likely to want to watch and photograph than catch and record.

The Porbeagle shark is a close cousin of the feared Great White shark and in the 1970s Porbeagle fishing off Crackington Haven in North Cornwall was so prolific that boats used to queue to drift chum. Whenever I recall that situation, I think what a shame it was that those anglers were killing their catches, and not just observing them. With the numbers that used to exist then cage diving would have been possible as long as the sharks cooperated, and they would still be plentiful if they had been examined and admired rather than over-fished.

We have seen that annual catches of Blue sharks by the Looe angling fleet were once 2000, 3000, 4000, 5000…even, in one year, 6000 and, although the number has now dropped to fewer than 200, there are still angling boats that pursue both Blues and Porbeagles on Cornwall's north and south coasts. In South Africa's Western Cape yesterday's fishermen and trophy anglers have become today's shark guardians and eco-tourism operators. So why can't the same mentality rule in Cornwall and Devon? Although vastly depleted, we've still got the sharks, and we've got the angling boats, so why couldn't we do the same? If cage diving were to prove possible it would be a win for the sharks, a win for the skippers, a win for holidaymakers and shark enthusiasts – and a win for eco-tourism!

In August 2005, my wife, Jacqui, and I decided to see if shark eco-tourism would work in Cornwall. Together with groups of volunteers, we ran two pilot days out of Looe, aware of the sceptical glances of skippers peering suspiciously and doubtingly at our chum slick. No floats, no baited hooks, just the usual chum bags over the side and another one with a float on a line 15 metres astern. The first shark arrived after 40 minutes and the second an hour-and-a-half later. A large two-and-a-half metre Blue shark grabbed our bait bag and we had a tug of war. I lost, the bag ripped and our shark had breakfast, lunch and supper all in one go.

Cage diving in operation off Cornwall in 2006.   (STUART PATTERSON)

We steamed back to Looe and on the way I spotted and rescued a net-entangled porpoise. Two Blue sharks, a number of dolphins, and a porpoise rescue – not a bad day. The following weekend we drew a blank but one out of two is 50 per cent, and we decided to take the idea further and run a proper pilot project in the summer of 2006 with three Blue shark days out of Looe, and three Porbeagle days out of Bude and Padstow. We sent two press releases to the diving magazines which resulted in short, one paragraph items – and we also put the idea on our website. The response was phenomenal: the phone rang constantly and our email box filled up. Thereafter, we had to double our planned six days to 12 with six participants per day. All in all, around 2,000 people enquired after 72 places. There was no doubt that the interest in Cornwall's sharks was there!

The winter was spent planning and plotting. Two shark cages were built, and I designed a special 'hook over the gunnels' dive platform and steps. Many enquirers questioned the necessity of needing cages for Blues

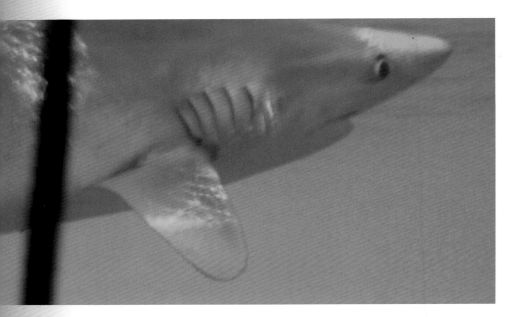

A man's eye view of a Blue shark cruising by the cage.   (M Boothman)

and Porbeagles. However, both are predatory animals and while, as far as I know, there are no confirmed records of Porbeagle attacks, there are records of Blues being dangerous to humans so safety was a vital factor. Other considerations were how to provide stability in the water in Cornwall's strong surface currents, and how to keep the sharks around the boats. In the past, I have deployed a rope line to hang onto, which, with a float on it tucked under an arm, provided hands-free anchorage but not total stability. Caging our participants not only provided total safety for both sharks and humans, but also solved the stability problem and enabled me to bait the animals safely right up to the cage.

I knew I could attract Blues to a cage, or to a swimmer, but Porbeagles are shy and my two previous attempts to get into the water with them had failed. One of those attempts gained me a brief glimpse and the other was a washout, resulting in no sighting at all. A human swimming around struggling to maintain position in a strong current is not going to result in calm sharks, and, generally, they are unlikely to hang around long after a snorkeller gets in the water. As soon as we started chumming,

I planned to put the cage into the water so there would be no splash or disturbance when the sharks arrived. I hoped then to slip our observers into the cage, and keep the shark around it. Provided conditions were flat enough, it seemed cages would be the best way forward for all these reasons.

The 2006 pilot project went well and a great deal was learned. The success rate in encountering Blue sharks was 66 per cent on the north coast. In 2007, we expanded the project to more than 50 days, which meant we could take out more than 300 participants. As it happened, a summer of unsettled weather meant that we lost half our planned days but the encounter success rate remained at a similar level. In short, we had proved the concept worked and that a profitable eco-tourism opportunity was there to be developed. Shark angling skippers from Cornwall, Devon and South Wales are the logical people to take this forward. In Cornwall and Devon the summer of 2008 was a 'summer most of us want to forget'. There were four boats ready to operate shark cage diving trips off the north coast and I was hopeful that south Cornish and Devon skippers would become interested. We planned 24 days of our own to keep interest active and encourage others to follow. We would normally reckon to lose 20% of our day trips to bad weather. In 2008 we lost 80%, a truly abysmal situation but when we did get to sea we saw sharks and our 65% success rate was maintained.

Provided the weather is fair a shark watching day-out off Cornwall or Devon can be a magical experience. Apart from the main targets of Blue or Basking sharks, it's possible that Porbeagle and Soupfin sharks will be encountered and there's even the thrilling prospect of a Mako turning up.

The South African model shows how economically important shark eco-tourism can be. In January 2008 my friend Craig Ferreira in South Africa told me that the twelve cage diving operators were generating over 70 million rand (£5,400,000) per year i.e. approximately £450,000 per operator. This is the direct revenue being taken by the operators, the value of the industry is much larger once all the tangential aspects have been considered. Hotel rooms, shuttle buses, restaurants, airlines, retailers, and a host of others benefit directly from tourists coming to South Africa to see sharks. We can do some similar figures for Cornwall.

In 2007 we had over 300 clients booked for cage diving at £95 per head. This is £28,500 of direct revenue and can be doubled if one assumes that each person spent another £100 in the county. We did only four days a week with six people a day, so on this basis it's easy to see how one operator working seven days a week, and taking out eight to ten clients daily would comfortably produce over £100,000 a year for himself and other benefiting businesses. I believe Cornwall could easily support ten operators which would mean a million pounds in revenue from cage diving; this figure would greatly increase were Basking shark watching revenue added. There are many operators in Cornwall who run Basking shark watching and diving excursions from June to September. Cornwall is one of the best places in the world to view the second largest fish in the sea.

You can only kill something once, so dead value is one time, whereas live value is a day after day income stream. I am a cynic and believe that mankind is such an awful out-of-control species that unless it's in his interest not to do so he will end up killing most wildlife. Money is a great incentive not to kill, it's simple "if it pays it stays" that's why we have to develop shark eco-tourism and give sharks a real live value.

A new twist to shark eco-tourism. (C WYLIE)

Chapter 5: Shark Attacks

If the term Shark Attack means a deliberate provoked or unprovoked incident, when a shark interacts with a human in an aggressive manner, involving the possibility of injury, then I have only managed to find one such incident in British waters. On June 1st 1971 a diver was working his way out from the beach at Beesands in south Devon. The diver, Jimmy Johnson, had to fend off two attacks with a lobster hook before making his way back into water too shallow for the shark to follow. Opinion is divided, some commentators believe the shark was a Mako while others favour a Porbeagle having been involved. An eye witness agrees with Johnson's account that he was attacked, and that a 3-metre (11ft 4in) shark was involved. The size estimate would more likely indicate a Mako, and the International Shark Attack File (ISAF) lists a total of 45 Mako attacks on humans but only three involving Porbeagles. The size estimate also points to a Mako as the world record Porbeagle was caught in British waters and this shark was smaller than both Johnson's and the witnesses estimates. There are many other 'attacks' in British waters and even shark-caused deaths. In Kent a shark mounted on the wall of a pub behind the bar fell off and injured the landlady! A Worcestershire chef ended up in hospital after a Blacktip shark in his restaurant's aquarium bit his wrist while being fed prawns. Darren Smith, a Newquay chef, was driving to a restaurant with a 7 ft Porbeagle on ice in the back of his van. He braked and the shark shot forward ending up on his shoulder. His attempt to push it back ended with his hand in its mouth which closed causing an injury needing 17 stitches.

Phil Hambridge from south Wales and Stephen Perkins were involved in separate incidents which resulted in their having to be helicoptered to hospital – Both were de-hooking Blue sharks, in Phil's case a tail flick sent a hook into the side of his head, while Stephen Perkins suffered serious loss of blood after being bitten by a shark from which he was removing his hook. Both anglers can be said to have provoked the incidents by hooking the sharks in the first place.

Shark-caused deaths occurred in Scotland in 1937 when a Basking shark overturned a small boat resulting in three deaths by drowning. Off

Porthkerris in Cornwall in 1956 a Basking shark blew up the Royal Navy! Commander Brooks and a crewman decided to kill what they thought was a dangerous shark. A Bolas type explosive device was rigged and thrown at the shark as it cruised passed their boat. The explosives were lit, the aim was good and the shark swam off with the ready to explode device across its back. The boat turned away from the impending explosion as the shark swum off. The animal then forgot its orders, turned around and swam back under the boat and blew it up killing two personnel.

The facts therefore indicate that in terms of shark attacks in our waters, the land is a more dangerous place to be than in the water, and boats are the most dangerous places, especially if you can't swim or try to blow up a shark.

Less than 10 humans are killed by sharks around the world every year. Man is catching up to 100 million sharks annually pushing many species to the brink of extinction.

(C WYLIE)

Chapter 6: Media Feeding Frenzies

Much of what we think about any subject is based on our daily diet of information from the media. And, of course, it is much more sensational for sharks to be portrayed as man-eating monsters than victims of over-fishing. The result is that the public is not just badly informed about sharks, it is often completely misled.

Why should it be front-page "news" that Mako sharks have been seen off the Cornish coast? They have been there for tens of thousands of years.

30p   THOUGHT: GET OUTTA THE WATER

JAWS U

Man-eating Gr
White sha
spotted
our co

By BRIAN FL

BANK holiday trip
Jaws alert after a
Great White shark v
off the UK coast.

The 15ft monster —
shark in Steven Spiel
buster movie — stalks
boat near Padstow, Co

The picturesque port
with family trippers du
Veteran shark fisherma
who saw the 15ft beast,
"I wouldn't be surprise
a surfboard or gobbled a
TV fishing show present

SHARK!

ust when you thought it was
safe to paddle in Padstow...
fierce Great White turns up

Shore looks scary . . . a shark like this Jaws monster is lurking off Cornish holiday beaches

By BRIAN FLYNN

FISHERMEN told last night of their terrifying Jaws-style encounter with a Great White shark.
The massive man-eater shad-
at off the Cor-

must have been a Great White because nothing else has jaws pow-erful enough.

Great Whites like the one in the movie Jaws are seen off Amer-ica's West and North East coasts.

It is a mystery why one has arrived off Cornwall.

But marine life expert Dr Tony Stebbing said there had been an increase in exotic species off Brit-

Too close for

Four saved from death's jaws — by a pod of dolphins

By Roger Maynard
in Sydney
and Toshi Sulaiman

FOUR swimmers who came face to face with a great white shark off the coast of New Zealand were saved by dolphins that came to their rescue.

The three-metre (10ft) shark came within two metres of the swimmers, all of whom are lifeguards at a surf life-saving club north of Auckland.

They were saved only after a pod of dolphins emerged from nowhere and circled them in a tight defensive formation for 40 minutes until the quartet were out of danger.

Only when the dolphins were sure that the shark had disappeared did they open out the tight circle and allow the lifeguards to swim back to shore.

The incident took place three weeks ago, but the swimmers kept quiet about the story until yesterday because they feared that the shark would be hunted.

The group had been swimming 100 metres off a beach at their home town of Whangarei, in North Island, New Zealand. Ron Howes, who went on the training swim with his 15-year-old daughter, Niccy, and two of her friends said that he was lucky to be alive.

He knew something was wrong when the dolphins appeared suddenly and started to herd them up. 'They pushed all four of us together by doing tight circles around us,' he said.

When he tried to break away from the protective group, two of the bigger dolphins herded him back. It was then that he noticed the shark cruising towards them.

'I just recoiled,' he said. 'I was only about two metres away from me, the water was crystal clear and it was as close as the nose on my face.'

At that point he saw what the dolphins were doing. 'They had corralled us to protect us,' he said. The dolphins appeared agitated, repeatedly slapping the water with their tails and ... whatever seemed to be trying to deter the shark.

Over centuries the affinity to hum...

...been
...become part of marine folklore and marine scientists said their behaviour was altogether surprising. Rose, from the ... Society International, ...

e great white accounts for up to half of shark attacks

FRIEND AND FOE

...LENOSE DOLPHIN
(...ops truncatus)

■ ...is smooth and light ...-grey in colour, with ...wn grey belly. Beak is ...d like a bottle
...ms in temperate and ...al waters worldwide
...st dolphins are on ...ge 8ft to 12ft and ...around 450kg. Males ...gger than females
...mmunicate through ...cks, whistles, snapping ...s, and leaping up to ... in the air
... fine sense of hearing, ...our sense of smell
...m in groups of up to ...wn as pods. Can ...orm herds of up to ...lphins.

GREAT WHITE SHARK
(Carcharodon carcharias)

■ Only its belly is white, it is grey or blue grey on top
■ Found along temperate coastlines around the world including California, Australia, New Zealand
■ Adults are generally between 10ft and 15ft long. The record is 22ft. Females bigger than males
■ Have 3,000 teeth at any one time. Do not chew their food, but rip off chunks and swallow them whole
■ Can swim through water at speeds of up to 43mph
■ About half to a third of known shark attacks each year are by great whites. Most are not fatal

---

THE DAY I WAS EATEN ALIVE

It's every swimmer's nightmare. In the week a surfer is butchered by a Great White, a British diver recalls his own terrifying shark attack

---

Bride's screams as her husband is eaten by shark

A BRIDE on honeymoon watched in horror as her husband was torn to pieces by a great white shark.

Tina Bayes stayed on the beach while her husband Cameron, 26, paddled out to sea on his surfboard off the coast of South Australia.

As he turned round to wave at her the 12ft shark struck and dragged him under.

Other surfers said the shark initially appeared to release Mr Bayes, who somehow managed to get back on his board.

Seconds later, however, it grabbed him a second time and he was not seen again.

The shark then surfaced 500 yards from the beach, where it appeared to spit out a piece of surfboard.

From **Richard Shears**
in Melbourne

yesterday off remote Cactus Beach, an area notorious for great whites.

Mr and Mrs Bayes, who were both New Zealanders, were on a working honeymoon in Australia.

Staying at campsites, Mr Bayes planned to earn money shearing sheep.

Surfer Jeff Hunter, who saw the attack, said: 'It was all very quick and very frightening.

'The shark had no hesitation. It took the surfer in a kind of circular motion.

'It looked horrendous,' Mr Hunter added. 'There was blood and surfboard everywhere.'

Mrs Bayes, who is also in her mid-twenties, was taken to hospital

famous highway which crosses Nullabor Plain between Adelaide ... Perth.

'They feed off several seal colonies about two miles from shore and ... low schools of salmon closer to sh...

Yesterday's attack was the f... death of a surfer at the bea... although a local boy bled to dea... 1975 after a great white shark bit his leg while he was swimming.

Local surfboard maker Paul G... elle said: 'Surfers are conscious of ... risk of shark attack but we've al... relied on the fact that there has n... been a fatality here.'

Shark expert Rodney Fox, ... needed more than 500 stitches a... surviving an attack off the South A... tralian coast in 1963, said he w... 'not feel comfortable' in the sh... infested waters of Cactus Beach.

30

New sighting 'of Great White'

IT WAS A MONSTER

...ea beast . . . the massive shark filmed swimming off Cornwall and (ab...

Trevor's awe over shark
...e caught on videotape

...OLIDAYMAKER Trevor
...essey told last night of the
...atic moment he caught a
...ent shark on videotape.

...Trevor, 50, spotted the beast
...m clifftop Tintagel Castle in
...rth Cornwall.
...he spot is only about 20 miles from...
...stow, where fisherman told...

EXCLUSIVE by BRIAN FLYNN

...fish they saw a Great White shark
...from their boat this week.

...And the creature was circling just
...100 yards from a beach where families
...with children were paddling.

...Dad-of-two Trevor said last night:
..."It was a monster. We were walk...
...to swimmers yester...
...after a 20ft great white
...shark attacked a cabin...

FINS YOU SHOULD KNOW

GREAT WHITE SHARK
SIZE: 19 and three quarters feet
COLOUR: Grey with white underparts
APPEARANCE: Pointed snout, streamlined
ATTITUDE: Aggressive
DIET: Fish, seals and dolphins

BASKING SHARK
SIZE: 34 feet, second largest fish
COLOUR: Dark grey to light black
APPEARANCE: Streamlined, large gills
ATTITUDE: Non-aggressive
DIET: Plankton

If the Great White is known as keen then its
cousin the Basking Shark should be called
GUMS — because it has no teeth. It eats
microscopic sea creatures called plankton,
sucking them in as it swims along. However...

THE DAILY TELEGRAPH

Italian beaches shut after shark attacks cruiser

By Bruce Johnston in Rome

THIRTY miles of beach
...long Italy's coast were
...ged to swimmers yester...

The Great
White Shark

Area closed

MARCHES

Adriatic Sea

ITALY

50 miles

...boat was shown on Italian
television at the weekend.

The white shark besieged
the cruiser on Thursday after
the fisherman and his son
Nicola, 10, caught a small
shark and strapped it to the
side of the boat.

Attracted by its blood, the
white shark suddenly
appeared in the water along...
"All at once, I saw this
large greyish fin," said Mr
Catalani, a farm manager.

After seizing a container
with bait, the shark then
turned its attention to the
strike. Luckily...

NEWS

...small shark. But after
devouring it, the white shark
began circling the boat.

Fascinated, Mr Catalani
filmed the entire incident
from the bridge and only
headed back to port at the
urging of his son.

Mr Catalani was later criti-
cised for failing to report the
incident immediately to the
nearest port authority to the
day, he said he informed the
skipper of a passing boat
and, amid laughter, was told
that "sharks should have left the
wine at home".

Authorities at the week-
end played down the danger
to bathers, saying that white
sharks rarely attacked
humans and preferred deep
water. However, an expert,
Giuseppe Notarbartolo, said:
"Everyone says sharks like
deep water. But it is a false-
hood that is convenient for
the tour agencies.

"In reality, the shark is a
typical predator of river-
mouths, and whose instinct
is to approach the coast to
strike.

overlooks humans." Corrado
Piccinetti, head of the Marine Biology Laboratory in
Fano near Senigallia, said:
"Sharks are erratic animals,
and they go where they...
find food...

Stefano Catalani, far right, with his 10-year-old son Nicola to...

...to eat. Perhaps he'll move
[north] to the Po delta."
Colin Speedie...
expert said...

Gamecard inside your TV mag

IS THIS JAWS?

Tripper films huge shark lurking off Cornish coast

By BRIAN FLYNN

A MASSIVE shark lurks
menacingly just
yards off a Cornish

31

It's not news that a hippopotamus is spotted in a river in Zimbabwe, it's not news that a lion is seen in Kenya or an elephant is seen in India. It's not news because it's normal that they should be there. It's also normal that sharks should be observed in the sea. If a shark was spotted sitting on an aeroplane landing at Newquay Airport that would be news! A shark chasing sheep on Bodmin Moor would be news, but a shark in the sea – where do journalists expect them to be?

Chapter 2 on Great White sharks recounted the extraordinary 2007 'Great White shark' incidents off St Ives reported by the *Sun* newspaper. A year later I discovered that this incident had produced an 18% increase in their daily paper sales figures. This is a powerful incentive to portray sharks as sensational bad guys. The summer of 2008 did not produce any Cornwall and Devon shark scare stories, but there was however a real beauty reported in the *Sun* from north Wales. A shark's tooth was washed up on an Anglesey beach, it was identified as having come from a Great White. The *Sun* got the story and portrayed this find as meaning that killer sharks were now roaming our coasts in search of victims! Reality check. The tooth displayed clearly had a hole drilled in it indicating it had been used as a piece of jewellery, probably on a neck chain.

(C Wylie)

A Blue shark and its reflection.

(RICHARD PEIRCE)

These dopey shark stories don't seem to deter holidaymakers from visiting Cornwall and Devon. In fact St Ives turned their 2007 shark scare into a great tourist attraction which produced significant tourist revenue. In 2003 Cheyney Hodgetts claimed to have seen a Great White from the cliffs at Baggy Point in north Devon. Local skippers ran packed trips to the spot where the 'Great White shark' had been seen.

CHAPTER 7: Strange and True

Little known shark facts

- A Cornish fish merchant was slightly surprised when, having bought a Porbeagle shark, he cut it open and found a whole pigeon inside. The pigeon's leg ring enabled its owner to be contacted, and he was amazed when he learnt where his pigeon had landed!

- Mermaid's purses found on Cornwall and Devon's beaches are egg cases that may well have contained baby sharks.

- The 'rock salmon' we see on sale in British fish and chip shops is actually shark – Spurdog shark.

- In 1961 the Shark Angling Club recorded 6000 Blue sharks caught off Looe in Cornwall by boats reporting to the club. In 2008, the figure was 152.

- Blue sharks caught and tagged off Cornwall have more than once been re-caught off the eastern United States.

- There is much speculation about how the Porbeagle shark got its name, and there are many theories. One is that it comes from the Cornish "porth" for harbour and "bugel" meaning shepherd.

- The Mako is said to be the fastest shark. Swim speed estimates vary from 20mph to 50 mph.

- Basking sharks may well filter more than 1800 cubic metres of water an hour. That is roughly the equivalent of an Olympic swimming pool.

- From *Shark Attack* by H. David Baldridge. 'In reply to a question concerning the Royal Navy's wartime need for an effective shark repellent, Prime Minister Winston Churchill assured the House of Commons that "….the British Government is entirely opposed to sharks"'.

- Male Blue sharks are very aggressive during mating and grip the females with their teeth during the process. However, female Blue sharks have skin two-to-three times the thickness of males to give them some protection during these amorous encounters.

- Legend has it that Blue sharks will follow a ship on which someone has died waiting for the body to be committed to the sea.

Porbeagles in crates in Newlyn market awaiting sale. (JED TREWIN)

Piles of dead sharks photographed in Vigo, Spain. Many of these Blue sharks will have travelled south into the Bay of Biscay from Cornwall.

(JOHN NIGHTINGALE)

Chapter 8: The Future of our Sharks

Few creatures on land or sea have been as unsustainably and often cruelly exploited as sharks. All the large species found in our waters are seriously depleted and many of our smaller sharks are also listed as threatened or critically endangered.

Blue shark cruises past the cage off Cornwall.   (Mark Boothman)

Research carried out by the Dalhousie University in Nova Scotia, Canada, has produced figures based on 15 years of catch reports from the western Atlantic. Regrettably, there is no similar research for the eastern side of the Atlantic. However, it is reasonable to assume that for some species the position is similar and, for others, virtually the same. The Blue shark, for example, is involved in a continual circular migration around the north Atlantic and is one population, and so the western Atlantic figures will probably apply to the eastern side. Fishing pressures on sharks have not slackened since the research was published so the depletion rates today are likely to be even higher. The Dalhousie figures relevant to some species found in Westcountry waters are as follows:

Blue shark – depleted by 60 percent
Shortfin Mako – moderate decline
Thresher shark – depleted by 80 percent
Hammerhead shark – depleted by 89 percent
Spurdog shark – depleted by over 90 percent

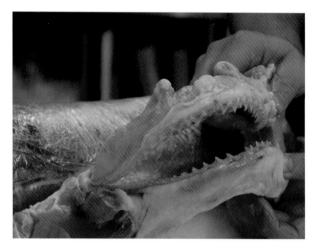

Jaws and steak from a Thresher shark landed in Exmouth in summer 2008 on sale at Darts Farm, Devon.
(A Bennett)

Different species are caught for different reasons, but the single most important reason that most large sharks are caught is for their fins. As the economies of China and other Far Eastern nations have developed, shark fin soup has become an affordable luxury for an ever-increasing market. And, shamefully, the European Union is one of the largest suppliers of fins to those markets. Spanish fishing fleets harvest enormous numbers of sharks and supplied about 11 per cent of the total Hong Kong fin market in 2005. The number of fins supplied by Great Britain is thought to be negligible.

The high value of fins has meant that sharks have ceased to be nuisance by-catch, which, if put back, would have a chance of survival. Instead, they have become a highly valuable targeted catch. Longline fishing boats traditionally targeted tuna, swordfish, marlin, and others. Lines of more than 20 kilometres are usual with baited hooks every two to three metres. The deployment of just one line can catch hundreds of sharks. And, to ease storage and transportation problems and avoid taking the time required to kill the shark (as well as not having the risk of shark flesh tainting other fish), the sharks are often finned and thrown back into the ocean while still alive.

The Porbeagle shark is very vulnerable to over fishing due to its tendency to aggregate (form groups). This makes it easy prey for longliners. Two recent cases of large Porbeagle catches by longliners in the UK were in 2003, when one longliner was reported to have taken more than 130 sharks off south Cornwall, and in August 2007, when another took between 60 and 90 sharks near Lundy Island off north Devon.

In 2005, a Lowestoft-based company was planning a specific trade in Soupfin sharks. Like Porbeagles, Soupfin sharks (Tope) have a tendency to school that makes them vulnerable to over fishing. However, the venture was shelved, partly due to the efforts of various activist groups, and partly for economic reasons.

Sharks have been on our planet for some 400 million years. In comparison man is a real newcomer, if shark populations don't stop being unsustainably exploited extinction is around the corner for many species. The moral argument says we should stop over-fishing our sharks, but so does self-interest and humans usually respond to self interest. Healthy oceans are vital to a healthy planet, healthy oceans need robust intact food chains to keep them healthy. Sharks are apex predators – the top links in the chain – take out the top links and the chains collapse and re-adjust, but how healthy will the adjusted seas be? Sick oceans could herald a seriously ill planet.

The European Union Community Plan of Action for Sharks (CPOA) was adopted in February 2009. This plan of action provides measures to protect vulnerable species by reviewing the finning legislation, and proceeding according to scientific advice which will lead to more effective and appropriate management. The Angel shark, Porbeagle and Spurdog will all benefit when the CPOA is fully implemented.

Blue sharks caught off Looe in July 1955. Sharks caught off Looe are no longer killed but are returned live to the sea.

(SHARK ANGLING CLUB)

CHAPTER 9: Cornwall & Devon Shark Directory

Of the over 30 shark species found in British seas it's probably fair to say that about half (16) are found in Cornwall and Devon's coastal waters. I have excluded the Greenland shark and most of the deepwater sharks. The Smooth Hammerhead is rare as is the Bramble shark but these are confirmed in Cornwall and Devon records. I have found no confirmed Sixgill or Sevengill records, but they are on the British list, and there is every reason to believe these inhabit Cornwall and Devon's waters.

ANGEL SHARK

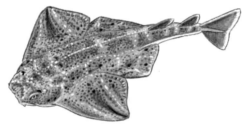

This shark had the sad distinction of being the first British shark to be declared locally extinct when the 2007 International Council for the Exploration of the Sea (ICES) conference declared the Angel shark locally extinct in the North Sea. Very rare now in Cornwall and Devon waters.

BASKING SHARK

The second largest fish in the world is a plankton eater, truly a gentle giant and often seen in Cornwall and Devon's waters in the summer months. Basking shark watchers don't even have to get wet, as these sharks are readily seen on cliff walks and from boats.

BLUE SHARK

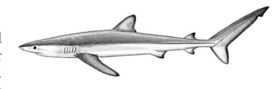

These beautiful and graceful sharks once existed in far greater numbers than they do now. Sustained over-fishing has depleted their numbers by over 60%. A Cornish illustration comes from the Looe Shark Angling Club whose annual angling catch figures have dropped from 2000 – 6000 right down to 149 in the 2009 season.

BLUNTNOSE SIXGILL

Another really large shark, the Bluntnose Sixgill reaches lengths of up to 4.8 metres (15ft). Not as sharky looking as a Mako or a Blue shark but an impressive animal.

BRAMBLE SHARK

Visitors to Cornwall and Devon will only have a slim chance of seeing this shark in fish markets. I have only seen dead specimens – one in a photo in Looe and the other in Newlyn fish market. The two dorsal fins and blotches on the back and sides make this shark easy to identify.

Porbeagle shark, found all around Cornwall and Devon's coasts.
(SHARK CONSERVATION SOCIETY)

NURSEHOUND SHARK

The Nursehound is common and
readily encountered on angling trips off the Cornwall and Devon coast.
Also known as the Huss or Bullhuss this is a handsome animal although
its names don't sound very sharky.

PORBEAGLE SHARK

A close cousin of the Great White
shark, really our own Great White
but smaller. The world record
Porbeagle was caught off Dunnett Head in the far north of mainland
Scotland in 1993 by Chris Bennett. Weighing 230kg (507lb) this 11ft
female was getting into the size range of her feared cousins. Porbeagles
are found all around Britain's coasts but north Cornwall is recognised as
one of the best places to see this impressive shark. The Shark
Conservation Society (SCS) is at the time of writing, half way through a
five year research, filming and photographic programme off north
Cornwall.

SHARPNOSE SEVENGILL
SHARK

Easily identified by its seven gills
this shark mostly inhabits deep
water. This shark is listed as 'near threatened' by the UN and is rare and
very unlikely to be encountered by visitors to Cornwall and Devon even
on fish market visits.

SHORTFIN MAKO SHARK

The International Shark Attack
File (ISAF) lists 45 Mako attacks
on humans. With the possible
exception of the 1971 Jimmy
Johnson incident (see chapter 5), there has never been a Mako attack in
British waters. Our water temperatures are at the edge of this shark's

Blue shark weights are now estimated at sea so there is no longer any need for the fish to be killed and brought back in for weighing. All sharks caught by the Shark Angling Club of Looe are now released alive. (SHARK ANGLING CLUB)

temperature preference, and they can now be considered a relative rarity in our Cornwall and Devon waters.

There have been only a few landings in recent years but I am aware of 5 sightings reports off Cornwall in the last four years that I would consider credible. The Mako is probably the fastest shark, and is a real fighting fish much prized by anglers. When caught on rod and line this shark often makes a series of athletic leaps taking it clear of the water as it fights for freedom. Cornish shark angling skippers believe the Mako is the most intelligent shark of all.

SMALLSPOTTED CATSHARK

Our smallest shark, and to my mind our prettiest. This gorgeous little fish is the only shark in British waters not considered to be under threat from over fishing. It does well in captivity and often breeds in our aquariums. From time to time the Blue Reef Aquarium in Newquay and the National Marine Aquarium in Plymouth exhibit this shark which, confusingly, is also known as the Lesser Spotted Dogfish.

SMOOTH HAMMERHEAD

There are very few confirmed sightings of the shark in our waters, however Cornwall and Devon are where most of the incidents have occurred.

SMOOTHHOUND SHARK

The Smoothhound is another aquarium favourite which breeds in captivity. Its crushing teeth are specially adapted for its diet of shellfish, and this shark spends most of its time cruising the sea floor.

STARRY SMOOTHHOUND

Almost identical to the Smoothhound but distinguished

by small white dots and spots (stars) on its back and sides. The Starry Smoothhound also does well in captivity and its numbers are not as threatened as most of our other sharks.

* N.B. (Recent research based on DNA shows that UK waters may be home to only the Starry Smoothhound and not the Smoothhound. It is likely that Starry Smoothhounds without spots have, in the past, been misidentified as Smoothhounds).

SOUPFIN SHARK

Also known as Tope, School shark, Vitamin shark and the Oil shark, this fish is found all round Britain's coasts. History was made in 2002 when an albino Soupfin shark was caught 129 km off the Cornish coast. Albino sharks are rare and so there was great excitement when this ghostly looking creature turned up in a net. Tagging programmes have established that this shark is a long distance traveller and a journey of 1770 km is recorded.

SPURDOG SHARK

Another shark with lots of aliases, also known as the Spiny Dogfish, Piked Dogfish and the Doggy. Overfishing has placed this shark high on the endangered list as its population is now thought to be only 3% - 5% of the size it was 50/60 years ago. 'Dogfish' doesn't do this two-metre shark any justice as it's a handsome animal, and in fish and chip shops is often described as 'rock salmon'. The Spurdog needs help and protection fast if it is not to follow the Angel shark into local extinction.

THRESHER SHARK

The Isle of Wight may be the best place to catch Threshers in British Seas but Cornish waters produced the largest Thresher ever caught in November 2007. This giant weighed a colossal 510kg (1122lb) and had a body length of five metres and a total (inc. tail) length of ten metres. At auction she made less than

£200 and later ended up in a landfill site.

In June 1981 a 181kg (398lb) Thresher shark surprised an Isle of Wight angling party when it decided to join them aboard their boat. The shark had been stalking the boat for an hour prior to breaching and ending up on board. Sadly the shark was too heavy to be lifted back over the side and into the water and had to be killed.

I have never seen a live Thresher in our waters and so was immediately jealous when my friend Phil Britts, master of the Padstow based *Blue Fox*, texted me in September 2007 to tell me he had a large four-and-a-half-metre Thresher swimming around *Blue Fox* while angling off Trevose Head. One day …I live in hope.

Porbeagle shark off North Cornwall.   (ROB ALLEN)

November 2007, 510kg (1122 lb) 5 metre world record Thresher shark
caught off Land's End. (RORY GOODALL)

Useful Shark Contacts

WEBSITES

American Elasmobranch Society .... www.elasmo.org

ElasmoFrance .... www.fredshark.net

Elasmo.com .... www.elasmo.com

Fishbase .... www.fishbase.org

International Shark Attack File .... www.flmnh.ufl.edu/fish/ISAF/ISAF.htm

Italian Research Group .... http://digilander.libero.it/infogris/

Mediterranean Shark Site www.zoo.co.uk/-z9015043

Reef Quest Centre for Shark Research .... www.elasmo-research.org

Richard Peirce .... www.peirceshark.com

Shark Conservation Society .... www.sharkconsoc.com

Shark Cornwall .... www.peirceshark.com

Shark Research Institute .... www.sharks.org

Shark Trust .... www.sharktrust.org

PHONE NUMBERS

Shark Cornwall (Cage diving) 01288 352608

Shark Angling Club 01503 262642

Mantis (Bude) Shark angling boat 07977 423511

Lady Mary (Padstow) Shark angling boat 07976 292379

Elemental Tours (Penzance) 01736 811200

    (Basking shark watching) .... or   07971 540280

Porthkerris Divers (Basking shark diving) 01326 280620

Atlantic Divers (Cage diving) 01637 850930

Marine Discovery (Penzance)

    (Basking shark watching) 01736 874907

Shark Trust 01752 672020